Big Win for Quin

For my nephews,
Parker, Henry, Anders, Aiden, Ajay, James, Davis, and Eli.
They are great at sports and at learning self-government.

And, for Quin; my first born and my buddy.
What would I do without you?
You have really mastered accepting consequences.
I remember when you used to have tantrums.
Then we learned the four basic skills. Well done son!

Special thanks to Ian Vassilaros who made sure my words came out
grammatically correct and offered kind suggestions.

Text Copyright 2013 by Nicholeen Pond Peck
Illustrations Copyright 2013 by Becky Fawson
Cover and book design Copyright 2013 by Becky Fawson

Published by Teaching Self-Government in Tooele, Utah

Teaching Self-Government
302 West 730 South
Tooele, UT 84074

http://teachingselfgovernment.com

Printed in the USA

ISBN 9 781892 131294

by Nicholeen Peck

illustrated by
Becky Fawson

**Teaching
Self-Government**

"Go Quin!" said Mom from her bench, far away.
Quin's family loved cheering on baseball game day.

"Get close to the plate!" Coach Brown called out.
But, Quin didn't move; his face showed no doubt.

He held the bat tight, and stood up quite tall,
While keeping both eyes fixed right on the ball.

"Strike one! Strike two! Strike three! You're out!"
Quin turned to the Ump with a loud, angry shout:

"I'm not out just yet, Mr. Ump! Can't you see?
That last pitch he threw was really ball three!"

"You're shouting at me—better watch yourself, son,"
The umpire warned him. "This game should be fun.

"You need to stay calm and say 'okay.'
Consequences happen almost every day.

"You should have stepped close to the plate in the way
Coach Brown told you to at the start of the play."

Accepting a consequence is hard to do!
For Quin, this skill was totally new.

When he made mistakes (as he often did),
He'd yell and stomp and blame other kids.

Next day, Dad told Quin to sweep the garage floor,
But Quin didn't want to finish that chore.

"Just now I instructed you to sweep up the floor,
But Quin, you said 'no' and walked out the door.

"You should have stayed calm, and said 'okay,'
Then swept up the floor and checked back right away.

"Since you chose not to sweep, you've now earned a new chore.
You'll weed in the yard when you're done with the floor.

"Okay?" asked Dad with a voice calm and cheery.
"Okay," said Quin, all grumpy with fury.

Quin wasn't okay. In fact, he was cross.

To him, his consequence was a double loss.

He swept up the floor and pulled the weeds too,
But he got mad and blamed Dad for chore number two.

If he'd accepted his consequence, Quin would be glad;
'Cuz then there'd be time to play catch with his Dad.

Quin's sister, Paije, was his very best pal,
But one day, they argued when Quin made a foul.

While throwing the basketball out in the yard,
Quin hit Paije on the back - really hard!

When the siblings were shouting, Mom came to discuss
How they should have behaved instead of the fuss.

"Just now you played rough and then someone got hurt,
When an argument started right here in the dirt.

"You should have been kind when you played man-to-man,
And disagreed appropriately when trouble began.

"Since neither of you chose to calmly disagree,
You've both earned extra chores to fold some laundry."

"Okay!" said Paije with calm voice, face, and body.
While folding she said to her brother, "I'm sorry."

"Oh, great," said Quin, with his chin to his chest.
"Yet another chore. Will I ever get rest?"

"You're pouting," said Mom without surprise.
"You should stay calm and look in my eyes,

"And say 'okay,' do the task, then move on.

You don't earn extra chores when you choose to stay calm."

While folding some towels, Mom then said to Quin,
"There's a special secret to getting a big win.

"Accepting a consequence hits a home run
With your Mom and Dad, so you can have fun

"Doing the things that you want to do,
Instead of complaining and feeling so blue.

"Consequences happen every day;
While at school, or at home, or with friends, or at play,

"Like striking out when you're up at the plate,
Or missing your breakfast when you wake up too late.

"Even though a consequence may not seem smart,
Accepting it always brings joy to your heart.

"Happiness has to be chosen, my son.
When you stay calm, your sadness is done.

"The key to your freedom (and happiness too),
Is the self-control inside of you.

"Accepting a consequence is like…a home run!

The steps are the bases, starting with one.

1. **Look at the person**
   – you're at the plate.

2. **With calm face, voice, and body**
   – first base is great!

3. **Say "okay" at second**
   – disagree appropriately works, too.

4. **Do your consequence at third**
   – you're almost through.

5. **Now to home you run**
   – drop the subject. You're done!

Accepting a consequence makes you #1!

Quin said, "I can do that! That plan sounds okay,

But I might have to practice a bit every day."

Mom said, "I'll practice with you – it'll be fun!

And each day, we'll hit a family home run."

That night after dinner, Quin stood and forgot
To clean up his dish and straighten his spot.

Dad saw the mistake and he motioned to Quin -
"I'm going to correct you. Are you ready? Let's win!"

Quin looked at his Dad, looked him right in the eye
With calm face, voice and body. No, he wouldn't cry!

With calmness and love, Dad corrected Quin well.
Then Quin said, "Okay." He did not even yell.

The family watched. The family waited.

Would Quin be okay? Would he be irritated?

Quin thought for a second, then turned to the task.

He cleaned up his plate, and his crumbs, and his glass.

His face was okay; he actually looked calm.

So Dad said, "Nice job! Now give me some palm."

He gave a high five, then moved on to task two.

His extra chore would be quite easy to do.

His task was to clean the double glass doors.

Smiling, he said, "...one of my favorite chores!"

Quin dropped the subject, his heart stayed glad.

When he was done, he reported back to his Dad.

"I did it!" he said, "Is there anything more?

I won! I'm happy and I'm done with my chore."

"Home run!" exclaimed Dad. And Mom said, "Grand slam!"

Quin smiled, took a bow, and said, " Aw, thank you, ma-am."

Next baseball game day, Quin struck out yet again.

But this time, he said "oh, okay" with a grin.

His family cheered louder than ever before

When they saw him stay calm, say "okay", and no more.

Coach Brown was surprised and he smiled real wide.

Quin sat in the dugout feeling joy deep inside.

"I did it!" he thought. "I just knew that I could.

Accepting a consequence feels really good."

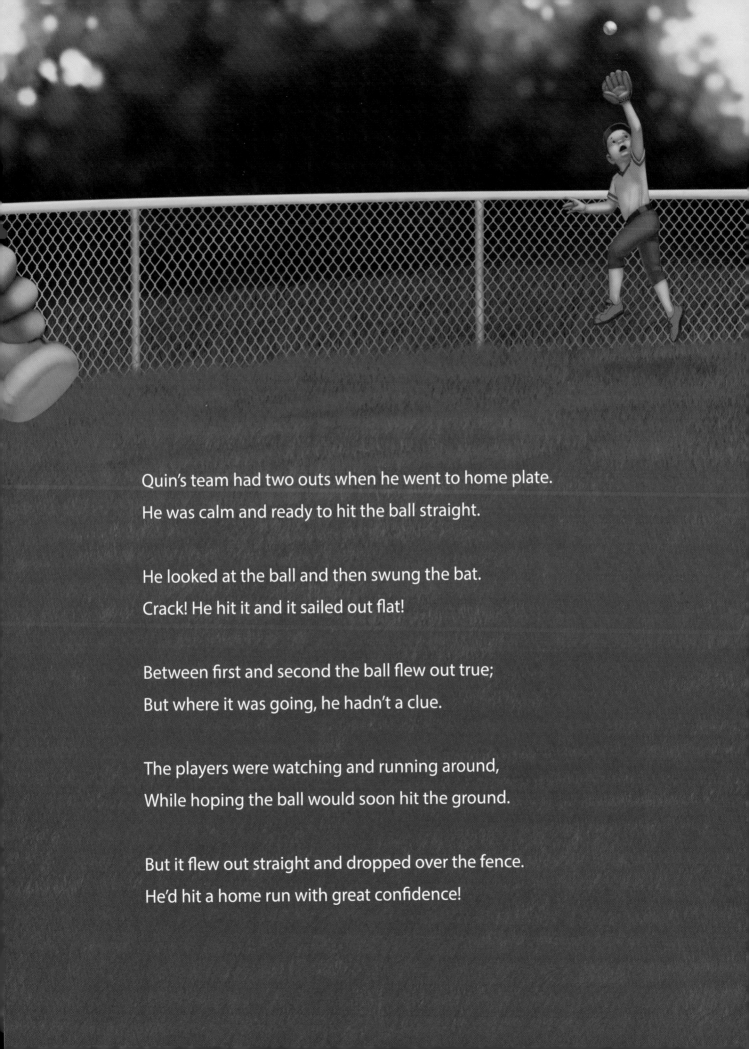

Quin's team had two outs when he went to home plate.
He was calm and ready to hit the ball straight.

He looked at the ball and then swung the bat.
Crack! He hit it and it sailed out flat!

Between first and second the ball flew out true;
But where it was going, he hadn't a clue.

The players were watching and running around,
While hoping the ball would soon hit the ground.

But it flew out straight and dropped over the fence.
He'd hit a home run with great confidence!

As Quin ran the bases, he thought of the steps.
He knew how to accept the next consequence.

1. ## Look at the person
    – you're at the plate.

2. ## With calm face, voice, and body
    – first base is great!

3. ## Say "okay" at second
    – disagree appropriately works too.

4. ## Do your consequence at third
    – you're almost through.

5. ## Now to home you run
    – drop the subject. You're done!

Accepting a consequence makes you #1!

Quin did drop the subject. He chose not to boast.

He smiled at his fans and said, "Thank you," at most.

But something had changed in Quin's ten-year-old heart.

He knew this new skill was only a start

Of freedom and happiness wherever he went.

Accepting a consequence was no accident.

Note To Parents:

Just like this story says, "Consequences happen almost every day." There are natural consequences such as hunger when you don't eat your dinner. There are synthetic consequences such as when you earn an extra chore for not following instructions or not disagreeing appropriately. Even though it would be ideal for children to understand natural consequences and make correct choices based on that understanding, most children have to be taught to see consequences first. And, natural consequences don't often happen quickly enough for cause and effect to be learned immediately. So, to prepare a child to accept all the natural consequences life offers, it is best to get into the habit of accepting synthetic consequences starting at a young age, while parents regularly draw attention to the natural consequences as well.

Consequences and punishments are very different from each other. Children are punished by being grounded or put in time-out, but they often don't accept it by arguing or sulking. So the punishment is usually accompanied with tones of anger and frustration instead of feeling calm and deliberate.

Children cannot learn self-government unless they are given the opportunity to accept a consequence. When children calmly say "okay" and complete their consequence, they are saying to themselves that they know they made the wrong choice. They are responsible for their choices. They are also able to show themselves that they can be calm and self-govern. They choose their own success. Allowing children to accept a consequence is merciful and loving.

When children refuse to accept the consequence after prompted to do so and after being corrected and given another negative consequence (chore), they are "out of instructional control." This means you would need to use either the toddler calm down method described in *Parenting: A House United* or a version of the Rule of Three if the child is older that six. After these calming exercises, the child would be calm enough to accept all the consequences earned. People of any age can't accept consequences and take personal responsibility for actions if they are upset or making excuses.

This book, *Big Win For Quin,* is the third book in a series of four books. The previous two books are called *Londyn LaRae Says Okay,* and *Porter Earns a Quarter.* These books teach following instructions and accepting no answers. The last book in this series will teach how to disagree appropriately.

Each of the children's books in this series teaches one basic skill and one way parents can teach their children. So, the children and parents should each come away with skills to practice. In *Londyn LaRae Says Okay,* parents learned about praising effectively. We see this again in this story. In *Porter Earns A Quarter,* parents learned about pre-teaching. In this story, in the dining room scene, we see Dad pre-teach Quin to prepare him to accept the consequence. New to *Big Win For Quin* is seeing effective corrections being done by Mom and Dad. (Although the rhyme does simplify the wording some.) The last book in this series will teach dealing with out of control behaviors.

The steps to correcting are: 1. Describe what happened ("Just now..."), 2. Describe what should have happened ("What you should have done was..."), 3. Tell them what they earned ("Since you chose....you have earned....Okay?"), 4. Praise & Practice it the right way (role play three times).

The whole point to learning self-government is to be happy and free. Happiness occurs when children choose the right and have open conversations and connections with Mom and Dad. Freedom comes when children conquer their excuses and accept the effects of their own choices. Freedom is also found when children know a skill -- such as accepting a consequence -- that they can use when difficult or stressful moments occur.

For additional help, please consult the Ten Step Teaching Self-Government Implementation Course on our website http://teachingselfgovernment.com . The course has videos, step by step audio classes, weekly calls with me, and comes with the book *Parenting: A House United,* which is the foundational self-government book that teaches the skills and principles necessary to learn self-government.

Nicholeen Peck

About the Author

Nicholeen Peck has been teaching self-government in countries around the world since 1999. She is the mother of four and former foster parent many times over. She has worked for the Utah Youth Village, has spoken for and on behalf of many parenting and family organizations, and was featured on BBC's World's Strictest Parents in 2009. She is the president of Teaching Self-Government, which offers coaching and courses in parenting to organizations and families around the world, and for which she has authored many books and articles. Other popular books by Nicholeen are Parenting A House United, Londyn LaRae Says Okay, Porter Earns A Quarter, and Popular Parenting Methods.

You can learn more about Teaching Self-Government at our website:
http://teachingselfgovernment.com

About the Artist

Becky Fawson loves children's picture books, especially books that are fun to read, inspire goodness and are beautifully illustrated. She loves teaming with writers and publishers, like Nicholeen Peck, who share a similar vision. After years as a freelance graphic designer, which included doing some editorial illustrations for magazines and cartoons for logos, Becky later received formal training in illustration at Southern Utah University. Becky and her husband live in Cedar City, Utah and enjoy time together with their children and grandchildren.

www.beckyfawson.com